How to Prepare For the STATE STANDARDS

VOL. 1

2nd Grade Edition

By Nancy Leininger

carney
EDUCATIONAL SERVICES

CARNEY EDUCATIONAL SERVICES
Helping Students Help Themselves

Special thanks to Rim Namkoong, our illustrator

This book is dedicated to:

The moms and dads who get up early and stay up late. You are the true heroes, saving our future, one precious child at a time.

All the kids who don't make the evening news. To the wide-eyed children, full of love, energy, and wonder. You are as close to perfection as this world will ever see.

TABLE OF CONTENTS

2nd Grade Edition

An Overview of the Standardized Test

In the spring of 2005, almost all American public school students in grades 2 through 11 took a standardized test as part of each state's standardized testing system. This included non-English speaking children and most children who are in special-education programs. The purpose behind this test is to provide both the school districts and parents with information about how their children are performing compared with other children from across the country. Keep in mind that this is a test of basic skills. The test was written to assess the abilities of students only in specified areas of the curriculum. Each state test is a standardized test. This means that ALL children across the state take the same tests in the same way. The directions given by teachers are the same, as are the amounts of time given to complete each testing section.

Why do schools give this type of test?

The standardized tests tell schools how well they are teaching basic skills which all students need to be successful in the future. Schools receive data about how their students did individually and by grade level. They use this information to help make teaching decisions. For example, if students at the fourth grade level all did well in the spelling section of the test, but didn't do as well in the reading comprehension section, those teachers may want to change the emphasis of their language arts program. Standardized tests are valuable, since they are an objective way to measure how successfully schools are delivering the basis. The idea behind standardizing the test is this: if every child takes the same tests in the same way, then it is a fair way to compare schools and districts. If, for example, one school gave all it's students an extra 5 hours to complete the test, then it would be an unfair advantage given to those children.

Each State Department of Education has taken extraordinary measures to ensure that all children get the same experience when taking the test. All testing materials are to be securely locked in classrooms or administrative offices when testing is not in progress. All teachers are discouraged from discussing test questions. Some districts even have non-teaching school employees act as proctors in classrooms to make sure that the testing procedures were being exactly followed. Schools want objective data about how well they are doing their jobs. Parents want this information as well.

What subject areas do standardized tests seek to measure?

Students in grades 2-8 are tested in two main areas, language arts and math. The specific skills tested within language arts are reading comprehension, spelling, vocabulary, grammar, listening skills and study skills. The math sections of the test measures student mastery of the procedures such as math facts and computations, and then tests their ability to solve applied programs. Each standardized test contains sections that measure student knowledge in science and social studies.

In grades 9 through 11, students were also tested in various reading and math skills. Additionally, these students were tested in science and social studies.

What do my child's standardized scores mean?

In the fall, your child's school should have sent you a copy of his/her scores on the test. Scores for most students were reported on a form that shows National Percentile rankings. For example, if your child received a math problem solving percentile rank of 75, that means that s/he scored better than 75 percent of the national sampling of students at his/her grade level. Student performance on each standardized test is measured by comparing your child's individual scores to scores from a national sample. This sample was created during a 1995 test given to students at various grade levels from across the country. The students selected for this 1995 test were representative of all students in the country. Their scores created a set of "norm scores". Scores of all other students taking each standardized test can be compared against this set of scores. If your child got a percentile rank of 89 in spelling, they scored higher than 89 percent of the national sample. Obviously, this means your child ranks in the top 11 percent of students in the spelling section of the standardized test. A percentile rank of 50 would place your child in the middle of the national sample. As you can see, schools want to ensure that parents get scores that accurately reflect their child's abilities, rather than coaching given by school personnel. In this system, it is important that all students compete on a level playing field.

How valid are my child's standardized test scores?

This is where the controversy begins. Critics of standardized tests point to the inclusion of non-English speaking students in the standardized testing to make the case that results may not be reflective of a child's true abilities in the classroom. For example, if a Spanish-speaking child scores in the 15th percentile in study skills, it may be because s/he simply didn't understand the questions. Thus, his/her score is much lower than it would have been if s/he took the test in Spanish. Another undeniable fact about the standardized tests results was this: children from wealthier suburban school districts performed much better on the test than did children from inner city school districts. Critics of the test contend that wealthier schools in the suburbs have many advantages such as computers or after-school programs which could ultimately help their students' scores on any testing program.

Even with all of this controversy, though, it is still clear that the standardized tests results do tell us a lot about how well children have learned the basic information which schools are supposed to teach. Looking at your child's scores can tell you about their strengths and weaknesses in each of the subject areas tested. Since each Department of Education is committed to continuing standardized tests, you should use your child's current scores as a starting point for the future., You can, and should, assist your child in preparing to take the standardized test in 2005 and beyond. Certainly, the schools and teachers in your state are primarily responsible for preparing your child for this test. Yet, parents have an important role to play. This book will give you some valuable tools you can use in helping your child do their best on this very important standardized test. It is the job of the nations schools to teach the material presented on the standardized test, but your role as a reinforcer of skills and a supporter of your child's progress in school cannot be ignored.

This workbook will introduce and review many important skills with a focus on the curriculum studied in second grade. This curriculum is based upon the content standards for the state of California. The second grade student has had little experience with the standardized testing format. Therefore, exposure and practice will assist students taking the standardized test and provide them with self-confidence and with many test-taking strategies.

The parent/teacher can help prepare their children for a more successful testing experience in school by spending short periods of time introducing and reviewing the practice pages in this workbook The workbook is divided into sections correlated to the subject areas covered in the standardized test. The workbook sections include specific directions, some skill strategies and testing samples.

This child should understand the skill before the practice test items are done. The parent may need to re-read and clarify for the child. If the child becomes frustrated, stop and review the concept and practice together. The pages in the workbook also include a variety of game-like activity worksheets and discussion topics for the parent and child. Making learning fun will maximize confidence and success when taking tests in school!

As the student is being guided through the various practice pages, a variety of strategies can be used to provide the student with tools to give them approaches to answering questions. The parent will need to assist with the directions and strategy techniques. Practice in reading questions, passages and recognizing typical standardized testing formats will allow the students to share their concerns and become comfortable with these student evaluation tasks.

Some key test taking strategies:

<u>Multiple Choice</u>

- Read the passage/question very carefully. Do you know the answer before you look at the choices? However, read all the choices and do not fill in the answer bubble until you have read all the choices.
- If you do not know which answer is correct, pick out the answers you know are **wrong.** Then, look at the remaining choices.
- Pick the best guess you can make. Always fill in an answer. If you leave a blank, it will be wrong. Your guess might be correct!

When reading the passages/sentences with the student and the student makes a mistake:

1. Say, "Try that again."
2. Say, "Did that make sense?"
3. Say, "Did what you read look and sound right?"
4. If the mistake makes good sense, don't worry about it!

How Your Child Can Improve Their Score On ANY Multiple Choice Standardized Test

Your child has entered an educational world that is run by standardized tests. Students take the Scholastic Aptitude Test (SAT) to help them get into college and the Graduate Record Examination (GRE) to help them get into graduate school. Other exams like the ACT and the PSAT are less famous, but also very important to your child's future success. Schools spend a great deal of time teaching children the material they need to know to do well on these tests, but very little time teaching children HOW to take these tests. This is a gap that parents can easily fill. To begin with, you can look for opportunities to strengthen your child's reading and vocabulary skills as well as their ability to follow detailed written directions.

The importance of reading:

Students who do well on standardized tests tend to be excellent readers. They read for pleasure frequently and have a good understanding of what they have read. You can help support your child as a reader by helping them set aside a regular time to read each and every day. As you may know, children tend to be successful when they follow an established pattern of behavior. Even 15-20 minutes spent reading a magazine or newspaper before bedtime will help. Children should read both fiction and non-fictional material at home, as well as at school. Ask your child about what they have read. Help them to make connections between a book they are currently reading and a movie or a television show they have recently seen. THE BOTTOM LINE: Children who read well will do better on standardized tests then children who do not. There is written material in all sections of the test that much be quickly comprehended. Even the math sections have written information contained in each question.

The importance of building a larger vocabulary:

As you may know, children who read well and who read often tend to have a large vocabulary. This is important since there is an entire section on all standardized tests that is devoted exclusively to the use of vocabulary words. You can support your child in attempting to improve their vocabulary by encouraging them to read challenging material on a regular basis. The newspaper is a good place to start. Studies have shown that many newspaper articles are written on a 4th to 5th grade reading level! Help your child to use new and more difficult words both in their own conversations and in their writings. If you use an advanced vocabulary when speaking to your child, don't be surprised if they begin to incorporate some of the new words into their daily speech. To be honest, one of the most immediate ways to judge the intelligence of anyone is in their use of language. Children are aware of this too. THE BOTTOM LINE: Children who have an expansive vocabulary will do better on any standardized test than children who do not. Find as many ways as possible to help build new words into your child's speech and writing.

The importance of following written directions:

Each state standards test is a teacher-directed test. Teachers tell students how to complete each section of the test, and give them specific examples that are designed to help them understand what to do. However, teachers are not allowed to help students once each test has begun. The written script for teachers seems to repeat one phrase continually: "READ THE DIRECTIONS CAREFULLY". This is certainly not an accident. Students face a series of questions that cannot be answered correctly unless the student clearly understands what is being asked for. Help your child by giving them a series of tasks to complete at home in writing. Directions should be multi-step and should be as detailed as possible without frustrating your child. For example: "Please take out the trash cans this afternoon. Place all the bottles and cans in the blue recycling bin and place all the extra newspapers that are stacked in the garage in the yellow recycling bin." If children are able to follow these types of directions and are able to reread to clarify what is being asked, they will be at a tremendous advantage when it comes to the standardized test. THE BOTTOM LINE: Children who are able to follow a series of detailed, written directions will have a tremendous advantage over those who are unable to do so.

All of the previous suggestions are designed to be used before the test is actually given to help your child improve in some basic test-taking skills. Here are some strategies that you can teach your child to use once they are taking the standardized test:

1. SELECT THE BEST ANSWER.

Each standardized test, like many multiple choice tests, isn't designed for children to write their own answers to the questions. They will fill in a bubble by the four answer choices and select the   BEST possible answer. Reading the question carefully is quite important, since the question may contain key words needed to select the correct answer. For example:

The first President of the United States was

    a. John Adams
    b. James Madison
    c. George Washington
    d. Thomas Jefferson

The correct answer is, of course, "c". Students would need to read the question carefully and focus on the key work in the question: "first". All of the names listed were Presidents of the United States early in our history, but only choice "c" contains the name of our first President. Looking for key words like "least" or "greater" will help your child to select the best answer from among the choices given.

2. ANSWER THE EASY QUESTIONS FIRST.

Each state standards test contains a series of timed tests. Children who waste time on a difficult question found at the beginning of a test may run out of time before they finish the entire test. A good strategy is to skip anything that seems too difficult to answer immediately. Once your child has answered every "easy" question in the section, they can go back through the test and spend more time working on the more time-consuming questions. If students are given only 30 minutes to answer 25 reading vocabulary questions, they shouldn't spend much more than a minute on each one. Wasting four or even five minutes on one question is not a good idea, since it reduces the amount of time your child will have to work on the rest of the test. Once time runs out, that's it! Any questions left unanswered will be counted wrong when the test is machine scored. Working on the easier questions first will allow your child to make the best use of the allowed time.

3. ELIMINATE ANY UNREASONABLE ANSWER CHOICES.

No matter how intelligent your child is, it is inevitable that they will come to test questions that they find too difficult to answer. In this situation, the best thing to do is to make an "educated guess". If students can eliminate one or more of the answer choices given, they have a much greater chance of answering the question correctly.

For example:
Select the word below that means the same as the underlined word:

The students were silent when the teacher was talking

    a. thinking
    b. quiet
    c. excited
    d. happy

Even if your child didn't know that "b" is the best answer choice, they could certainly eliminate choice "c" from consideration.

4. DO MATH QUESTIONS ON PAPER WHEN NECESSARY.

The math sections of each standardized test cause children problems because several of the answer choices seem like they could be correct. The only way to select the best answer choice for some math questions is to do the math calculation on scratch paper. The answer choices given for these questions are written to discourage guessing.

For example:

A mother dog weighs 70 pounds. Her puppy weighs 3 pounds. How many pounds do they weigh together?

    a. 703 pounds
    b. 10 pounds
    c. 73 pounds
    d. 103 pounds

The correct answer is "c", but it is hard to select the correct answer because all of the answer choices seem similar. Use scratch paper to determine the correct answer.

If you work with your child with these simple strategies, you will find that they will approach these test with confidence, rather than with anxiety. Teach your child to prepare and then to approach the standardized test with a positive attitude. They should be able to say to themselves; "I know this stuff, I'll do a great job today."

LANGUAGE ARTS

Content Cluster: READING COMPREHENSION

Objective: Students will read and understand grade-level appropriate material. They will draw upon a variety of comprehension strategies as needed (e.g., generating and responding to essential questions, making predictions, and comparing information from several sources). Students will use titles, tables of contents and chapter headings to locate information in expository text.

Parent Tip: When the student is reading and cannot figure out a word, remind the student to read around the word. Then, think about what makes sense. If there are pictures, look at them. Try sounding out the word parts. Make a good guess!
Another tip… When the student is stuck, instead of saying, "Sound it out" when an unknown word appears, help the student think, "Do I know a word that looks like this?" Tell the student to go back and reread all the words up to the tricky word and try again.

ACTIVITY

The table of contents below is from a book called <u>All About Abraham Lincoln</u>.
Use it to answer the questions.

ALL ABOUT ABRAHAM LINCOLN
Table of Contents

Chapter 1	Boyhood	Page 1
Chapter 2	Schooldays	Page 8
Chapter 3	Springfield Lawyer	Page 12
Chapter 4	Husband and Father	Page 16
Chapter 5	Political Career	Page 20
Chapter 6	Elected President	Page 25

1. What page does chapter 5 begin on?
   a. 12
   b. 16
   c. 20
   d. 22

2. Where would you find information about Mr. Lincoln when he was in second grade?

    a. Chapter 1
    b. Chapter 2
    c. Chapter 3
    d. Chapter 4

3. What chapter would tell about Mr. Lincoln as President?

    a. Chapter 1
    b. Chapter 3
    c. Chapter 4
    d. Chapter 6

TEST # 1

Read the table of contents and think about it.
Read the questions and choose the best answer.

ALL ABOUT GEORGE WASHINGTON
Table of Contents

1. Which chapter might tell you about where Mr. Washington went to school?
    a. 1
    b. 4
    c. 3
    d. 2

2. Chapter five might tell us about
    a. his home.
    b. his mother.
    c. his life as a military leader.
    d. his presidency.

3. What page would you begin to look for facts about his childhood?
    a. page 1
    b. page 14
    c. page 24
    d. page 28

ACTIVITY #1

Read the following short story. Think about what you read. Then, read the questions and choose the correct answer.

It was the first day of school. Summer vacation was over. Carrie had an upset stomach. Was she sick or just scared? Her mother told her to get her lunch and wait in the car. It was 8:00A.M. and finally time to go. When she arrived at school, her stomach felt like it had butterflies in it. She wanted to go home. Suddenly, she saw her best friend, Susan. Carrie kissed her mother and jumped out of the car. She was ready for school to begin.

1. Who was the main character of this story?
    a. Susan
    b. Carrie
    c. Mother
    d. None of the above

2. What word best describes Carrie's feelings on this day?
    a. Worried
    b. Sad
    c. Glad
    d. None of the above

3. What did Carrie take to school?
    a. Books
    b. Coat
    c. Lunch
    d. None of the above

4. What did Carrie do before she got out of the car?
    a. Turn off the radio
    b. Kiss her mother
    c. Cry
    d. None of the above

5. Why did Carrie jump out of the car?
    a. To catch the bus
    b. To see her best friend
    c. To go to the beach
    d. None of the above

ACTIVITY #2

Read the following short story. Think about what you read. Then, read the questions and choose the correct answer.

I have a favorite place. I love to go to the beach. I can swim in the water, jump in the waves and make sand castles. I like to listen to the birds and hear people playing together. Sometimes I bring my lunch and sit on a blanket and watch boats in the water. The sun feels warm and the wind feels cool. I can be happy at the beach all day long.

1. Who is telling this story?
    a. A cat
    b. A dog
    c. A car
    d. A child

2. Where is my favorite place?
    a. In the water
    b. In the sand
    c. At the beach
    d. None of the above

3. What is a good title to this story?
    a. The Waves
    b. My Favorite Place
    c. Fun in the Water
    d. None of the above

4. What feels cool in my face?
    a. Sun
    b. Wind
    c. Water
    d. None of the above

5. When I listen, what do I hear?
    a. The freeway
    b. Crying children
    c. The birds
    d. None of the above

ACTIVITY #3

Read the following short story. Think about what you read. Then, read the questions and choose the correct answer.

Boy Scout troop #72 was camping. The tents were set up and the boys were sitting around the campfire. Everyone was having fun except Ben. Ben was worried. He had never stayed out overnight. He was afraid of the dark and the noises of the night. He did not want the other scouts to know he was scared. They were all laughing and singing. Ben started to sing with them. Before long, he was laughing and having fun, too. He forgot about being afraid.

1. Where were the scouts going to sleep?
    a. In a hotel
    b. In tents
    c. On a boat
    d. None of the above

2. What was the scout troop number?
    a. 271
    b. 272
    c. 27
    d. None of the above

3. How did Ben feel about the noises?
    a. He liked them.
    b. He was mad.
    c. He was afraid.
    d. None of the above

4. Where were the scouts sitting?
    a. In the campfire
    b. Near the lake
    c. Around the campfire
    d. None of the above

5. What were the scouts doing that made Ben happy?
    a. Singing and cooking
    b. Playing and cooking
    c. Singing and laughing
    d. None of the above

ACTIVITY #4

Read the following short story. Think about what you read. Then, read the questions and choose the correct answer.

The day was cold. It had snowed during the night. Freddy couldn't wait to put his boots and mittens and coat on and go outside to build a snowman. He called his friend, Maria, and told her to come to his yard.

When Maria and Freddy started making the snowman, they rolled two big balls for the body and a smaller one for the head. They found sticks for the arms and rocks for the eyes and mouth. Freddy got a carrot for the nose and a hat for the head. It was almost 3 feet tall! They were proud of their snowman.

1. What would be a good title for this story?
   a. The Stormy Day
   b. Building a Snowman
   c. Fun on the Farm
   d. None of the above

2. Who are the children in this story?
   a. Freddy and Maria
   b. Andrew and Maria
   c. Erin and Freddy
   d. None of the above

3. When did it snow?
   a. In the morning
   b. After school
   c. In the night
   d. None of the above

4. How many snowballs did they use to make the snowman?
   a. One
   b. Three
   c. Two
   d. None of the above

5. How tall was the snowman?
   a. Three feet
   b. Five feet
   c. Four feet
   d. None of the above

ACTIVITY #5

Read the following short story. Think about what you read. Then, read the questions and choose the correct answer.

One summer day, Chris and Anne wanted to surprise their parents with breakfast in bed. It was going to be a special treat. They got up early and started making eggs and toast in the kitchen. Chris cracked the eggs in a bowl and stirred them with a fork. Anne put the bread in the toaster. Soon the trouble began.

The eggs spilled on the floor. The toast started to burn. The fire alarm went off, and their parents came running into the kitchen. The kitchen was a mess, and the surprise was ruined. Their father looked around and made a decision. They would all go out to breakfast and clean up the mess later.

1. What are the names of the children in this story?
   a. Tom and Mary
   b. Jeff and Chris
   c. Chris and Anne
   d. None of the above

2. What were they making for breakfast?
   a. Eggs and bacon
   b. Toast and eggs
   c. Eggs and juice
   d. None of the above

3. Why were they making breakfast?
   a. For mother's breakfast
   b. To make their father happy
   c. To surprise their parents
   d. None of the above

4. How did the trouble begin?
   a. The eggs spilled and the toast burned.
   b. The bacon was overcooked.
   c. The telephone rang.
   d. None of the above

5. Why did their parents run into the kitchen?
   a. They were hungry.
   b. They heard a dog.
   c. They heard the fire alarm.
   d. None of the above

Content Cluster: COMPREHENSION OF NONFICTIONAL TEXT

Objective: Students will read and understand a selection of nonfiction.

Parent Tip: Begin by reading the selection to get an idea what the story is about. When answering the questions, look back at the story to answer the questions.

ACTIVITY #1

Read the following selection. Think about what you read. Then, read the questions and choose the correct answer.

Earthquakes happen underground. They occur as often as a volcano erupts. The ground shakes. We can feel it. Houses move, and things can fall off tables and walls. This lasts only a few seconds, but it can cause much damage.

The earth has a crust like a pie does. The crust is made from sheets of rock. The crust floats on top of very hot liquids and more rocks. These liquids are always moving and cause pressure to build. Cracks present in the Earth's surface are called faults.

The sheets of rock feel this pressure. The sheets of rock push against each other. Sometimes the pressure is too much and the rocks shift. We might feel this movement. This is called an earthquake. After this happens, the rocks should not move again until the pressure builds again.

Geology is the study of earth. People who study the earth are called geologists. We know about earthquakes because of the work that geologists do.

1. This story is about a strong shaking called
   a. a hurricane.
   b. a tornado.
   c. an earthquake.
   d. a blizzard.

2. What pushes against each other?
   a. Water waves
   b. Sheets of rock
   c. Trees and plants
   d. Cars and bicycles

3. The Earth's crust is like
   a. a rug.
   b. a boat.
   c. a pie.
   d. a book.

4. A crack in the Earth's surface could be a
   a. road
   b. river
   c. lake
   d. fault

5. What would the best title for this story?
   a. Earthquakes
   b. Shaking and Breaking
   c. Rock and Cracks
   d. Pressure

6. Why is it important to know about earthquakes?

   a. So we can write stories about the weather.
   b. So we can understand what causes them.
   c. So we can play games better.
   d. It is not important.

7. An earthquake occurs as often as a

   a. volcano is erupting.
   b. thunderstorm is happening.
   c. football game is played.
   d. windstorm is happening.

8. The study of the earth is called

   a. biology.
   b. social studies.
   c. geology.
   d. meteorology .

ACTIVITY #2

When you go to sleep at night, one part of the animal world is just getting up. This is the world of nocturnal animals. Nocturnal animals are animals that are active at night.

Most of the nocturnal animal family comes out at night to look for food to eat. The dark of the night helps keep nocturnal animals safe. If an enemy is near, the nocturnal animal is hard to see.

The raccoon is a nocturnal animal. Some raccoons live on the ground, and some live in trees. Some live in forest-like areas near neighborhoods where people live.

Raccoons like to eat fish and fruit. They also like to eat corn and all kinds of seeds. They will also eat pet food and garbage in trashcans.

1. What are nocturnal animals?
   a. Ocean animals
   b. Pet dogs and cats
   c. Animals that are active at night
   d. None of the above

2. What do you think nocturnal animals do during the day?
   a. Eat
   b. Swim
   c. Sleep
   d. None of the above

3. What are nocturnal animals doing at night?
   a. Looking for food
   b. Building homes
   c. Playing games
   d. None of the above

4. Raccoons like to eat
   a. grass.
   b. fish, fruit and seeds.
   c. leaves.
   d. none of the above

5. Why might a bright moon be helpful to a raccoon's enemy?
   a. It is good for the enemy to sleep.
   b. It is easier for enemy to see the raccoon.
   c. The enemy runs faster in bright light.
   d. None of the above

ACTIVITY #3

In the United States, many people play football, baseball and basketball. But the best-loved sport in the world is soccer. Soccer is played in over 140 countries.

People love to watch soccer games. Sometimes crowds watching soccer games can be as large as 200,000 people. That is as many people as in a city.

Soccer rules are simple enough so even small children can play. It is safer than football, although the ball can be bounced off parts of the player's body. All you need is the right kind of ball. Almost any playing field will do. Players try to score goals by kicking the ball across the field.

Brazil has some of the best soccer teams. Soccer teams from Brazil have won the World Cup three times. The United States is becoming a bigger soccer country now. More and more people are playing the game every year.

1. The best title for this story is
   a. Ball Games.
   b. World Cup.
   c. Soccer.
   d. Brazil.

2. How many countries play soccer?
   a. Over 140
   b. About 14
   c. Only 40
   d. Don't know

3. Soccer balls can
   a. float on the lake.
   b. bounce off the bodies.
   c. roll down streets.
   d. be eaten.

4. What country has some of the best soccer teams?
   a. France
   b. Canada
   c. England
   d. Brazil

5. Players score goals by
   a. kicking the ball across the field.
   b. hitting the goal post.
   c. making a basket.
   d. touching the ball.

Content Cluster: COMPREHENSION OF RECREATIONAL SELECTIONS

Objective: Student should be able to read and relate to a character's situation and understand the story's purpose.

Parent Tip: Look for key words in the question. They will tell you where to find the answer in the story.

Read the following short story. Think about what you read. Then, read the questions and choose the correct answer.

Adam was going on a trip. It was his first trip alone without his mom and dad. He was going to visit his grandparents in another state. He was old enough to go on the trip without his family. He got on and found a seat near the window. Someone asked if he had his seat belt on. Soon there was a loud noise and he knew he was moving. He felt that he was going faster and faster and then up in the air. Adam looked out the window and saw the wing and some clouds next to him. He thought about his trip and seeing his grandparents, and he smiled.

1. How was Adam traveling?
    a. By car
    b. By boat
    c. By plane
    d. None of the above

2. Who was Adam going to see?
    a. His sister
    b. His grandparents
    c. His uncle
    d. None of the above

3. What was the loud noise he heard?
    a. The engines
    b. Thunder
    c. Crying
    d. None of the above

4. How did Adam feel about going on the trip?
    a. He was sad
    b. He was happy
    c. He was tired
    d. None of the above

5. How many times had Adam gone on trips without his parents?
    a. Two
    b. Three
    c. This was his first time
    d. None of the above

6. This story is most like a
    a. true story.
    b. tall tale.
    c. fairy tale.
    d. none of the above

7. What happened first in this story?

    a. He heard a loud noise.
    b. He got on and found a seat.
    c. He felt the plane moving.
    d. He say clouds next to him.

8. What time of year did this story take place?

    a. Winter
    b. Spring
    c. Summer
    d. Story does not say

9. How old do you think Adam is?

    a. two
    b. twelve
    c. twenty-five
    d. fifty

10. How long do you think Adam will be on the plane?

    a. several hours
    b. two days
    c. one week
    d. one month

Content Cluster: FUNCTIONAL

Objective: Students will read lists, directions, and visualize the steps for (real-life reading purpose) performing real-life tasks.

Parent Tip: Reading in order to perform a task requires specific strategies and skills not necessarily used with other kinds of text. Following step-by-step directions is a real-life purpose for reading. This simple set of instructions is similar to ones found in many children's books.

Read the following. Think about what you read. Then, read the questions and choose the correct answer.

BEAN PLANTS

You can grow pretty plants from beans that you can buy at the market.

Here is what you need:
    A bag of lima beans
    A clear jar
    Some soil and water

Here is what you do:
1. Wash some lima beans.
2. Fill the jar with soil.
3. Put the lima beans into the jar of soil. Place the beans near the side so you can see them inside the jar.
4. Water the beans in the soil.
5. Set the jar in a window. In a few days, you will see roots growing from the beans.
6. Soon after, you will see a tiny plant with a leaf or two sprouting up through the soil.

1. To grow the bean plants, you will need
    a. salt.
    b. music.
    c. soil.
    d. None of the above

2. What is the first thing that you need to do?
    a. Put the jar in the window.
    b. Wash the beans.
    c. Water the soil.
    d. None of the above

3. Why put the jar in the window?

    a. So the cat will not get it.
    b. So the beans can see outside.
    c. So it will get sunlight.
    d. None of the above

4. What do you usually see first after the beans start to grow?

    a. Roots
    b. Flowers
    c. Leaves
    d. None of the above

5. How long do you think it takes for the seeds to sprout?

    a. One month
    b. One year
    c. A few days
    d. None of the above

6. When the tiny plant begins to grow, what will you probably see first?

    a. beans
    b. flowers
    c. leaves
    d. None of the above

7. When a tree begins to grow, how does it begin?

    a. as a seed
    b. as a leaf
    c. as a root
    d. None of the above

Content Cluster: CAUSE AND EFFECT

Objective: Students will read and understand a story's purpose, make inferences, and tell what happened and why.

Parent Tip: When you read, sentences can tell what happened and why. Look at this sentence: The player fell, and the other team scored. What happened is the effect (the team scored). After you know what happened, you may have to think why. Some sentences do not give the reason. You have to figure out from the clues what the cause was.

Read each sentence. Choose the correct answer.

1. Jeff hurt his eye, so
   a. he watched TV.
   b. he went to the doctor.
   c. he played ball.
   d. None of the above.

2. It was hot outside, so
   a. I went swimming.
   b. I put on a coat.
   c. I made a snowman.
   d. None of the above.

3. The car stopped in the street, so
   a. I went to the park.
   b. I saw animals.
   c. I had to walk to school and call a tow truck.
   d. None of the above.

4. Because I exercise everyday,
   a. I am strong.
   b. I read a book.
   c. I work on my computer.
   d. None of the above.

5. Everyone stopped talking, so
   a. I jumped rope.
   b. the room got quiet.
   c. Tom started to eat.
   d. None of the above.

6. Because it was raining,

   a. I got wet.
   b. I walked to school.
   c. I went to the park.
   d. None of the above

7. When the sun comes out,

   a. the air gets cool.
   b. the air warms.
   c. the sky sings.
   d. None of the above.

8. Why is Juan happy?

   a. He fell down and hurt his knee.
   b. He has a lot of homework.
   c. It is his birthday.
   d. He must do his chores.

9. Jamila won the race because

   a. she ran fast.
   b. she read the paper.
   c. she ate candy.
   d. she is a girl.

10. Gilbert got his math all right because

   a. he watched T.V.
   b. he studied.
   c. he played games.
   d. he took a nap.

Content Cluster: READING VOCABULARY

Objective: Students will identify synonyms – words that mean the same or nearly the same.

Parent Tip: Encourage student to recall word meanings, skip difficult items, and go back to them later

---

Decide which word means nearly the same as the <u>underlined</u> word. Choose the correct answer.

1. <u>discover</u> the treasure
   a. see
   b. take
   c. find
   d. none of the above

2. <u>glance</u> at the story
   a. frown
   b. peek
   c. stare
   d. none of the above

3. a <u>clever</u> person
   a. loving
   b. little
   c. smart
   d. none of the above

4. a <u>gigantic</u> mountain
   a. small
   b. tiny
   c. huge
   d. none of the above

5. a <u>merry</u> song
   a. short
   b. sad
   c. happy
   d. none of the above

6. the <u>center</u> line

    a. middle
    b. left
    c. end
    d. none of the above

7. a <u>curved</u> line

    a. straight
    b. long
    c. bending
    d. none of the above

8. <u>trim</u> your hair

    a. cut
    b. grow
    c. help
    d. none of the above

9. <u>welcome</u> the guests

    a. close
    b. greet
    c. eat
    d. none of the above

10. a <u>wonderful</u> time

    a. awful
    b. some
    c. great
    d. none of the above

Content Cluster: CAPITALIZATION

Objective: Students will recognize errors in capitalization.

Parent Tip: Remind students that capital letters are used not only to begin a sentence but also used for names of days, months, people, and places

Read each line carefully. Find the word that should be capitalized. Then, choose the line that has a mistake in capitalization.

1. a. Look at this book. My
    b. teacher, mrs. King, gave
    c. it to me.
    d. All are correct

2. a. Will you celebrate my birthday?
    b. It is on Saturday, May 5th.
    c. We will have cake.
    d. All are correct

3. a. Have you read the story
    b. of goldilocks? She eats
    c. the bear's cereal.
    d. All are correct

4. a. Let's go to the park.
    b. Tori and I are meeting
    c. Emily and luke there.
    d. All are correct

5. a. Dad went to the airport to
    b. pick up Mom. she came in
    c. from New York.
    d. All are correct

6. a. If you wash the dishes,
    b. I will take you to the show. we
    c. will even get popcorn.
    d. All are correct

7. a. I can find california on the map.
    b. It is on the ocean and it
    c. is near Mexico.
    d. All are correct

Content Cluster: PUNCTUATION

Objective: Students will correctly use periods, question marks, exclamation points, and commas in sentences.

> **Parent Tip:** Share the following with your child. Reinforce the importance of following the directions and not going too quickly.

You use a period:
- To end a statement
- After an abbreviation such as Dr. or Mrs.

You use a question mark:
- To end a question

You use an exclamation point:
- To end a phrase or sentence that shows strong feeling

You use a comma:
- After each word in a series of three or more
- After a city name if the state follows
- After a greeting of a letter
- After the closing of a letter
- After the day of the month and before the year in dates

Read the following sentences. Think about what you read. Then, choose the line that has a mistake in punctuation.

1. a. Susan Tom, and Anne
   b. are going to Burbank,
   c. California.
   d. All are correct

2. a. Will your mom give us a
   b. ride home. My mom can't
   c. do it today.
   d. All are correct

3. a. We're going to a party for
   b. Jack and Jill.
   c. We're so excited?
   d. All are correct

4. a. February 12 2003
   b. Dear Mike,
   c. Please come to our party.
   d. All are correct

5. a. The flag of our country
   b. is red white and blue
   c. and has stars and stripes.
   d. All are correct

6. a. It will be
   b. a great trip to
   c. Fresno California.
   d. All are correct

7. a. We are really excited
   b. to go to Disneyland
   c. on my birthday?
   d. All are correct

8. a. Let's all try to
   b. do our best when we
   c. read write and do math.
   d. All are correct

9. a. Jose will go to
   b. Dr. Brown because
   c. he has a bad cold.
   d. all are correct

10. a. Kelly Bob Grant and Rosie
    b. want to play the game
    c. after school.
    d. All are correct

Objective: Students will recognize correct usage of words in sentences.

Try each answer choice in the blank to decide which one sounds right. Fill in the space for the word or words that best fit in the sentence.

1. Riley is _____ than Tom.
   a. tall
   b. taller
   c. tallest
   d. none of the above

2. They bought a bunch of _____ for their mother.
   a. flowers
   b. flowering
   c. flower
   d. none of the above

3. Lauren _____ the planes take off.
   a. watching
   b. watch
   c. watches
   d. none of the above

4. We use sleds to _____ on ice hills.
   a. slid
   b. sliding
   c. slide
   d. none of the above

5. Mrs. Ball _____ lifted the box.
   a. easily
   b. easier
   c. easy
   d. none of the above

6. I cut the apple into two _____.

    a. half
    b. halves
    c. halfed
    d. none of the above

7. That was a very _____ math problem.

    a. hard
    b. harder
    c. hardly
    d. none of the above

8. We _____ ball at recess.

    a. played
    b. plays
    c. playing
    d. none of the above

9. Amie was _____ a kite.

    a. fly
    b. flying
    c. flies
    d. None of the above

10. The dog _____ a hole in the yard.

    a. dug
    b. digging
    c. dugged
    d. None of the above

Content Cluster: SENTENCE STRUCTURE & CONTENT ORGANIZATION

Objective: Students will recognize sentence organization and structure.

> **Parent Tip:** The student must consider issues other than word or sentence level correctness. This test practice accommodates such matters as purpose, audience organization, structural elements, support, unity, and various modes.

How should these groups of words be written?

1. Alex hurt his foot. On the bike.
   a. Alex hurt his foot on the bike.
   b. Alex hurting his foot on the bike.
   c. Alex hurted his foot. On the bike.
   d. None of the above.

2. They coming are?
   a. Coming are they?
   b. Are they coming?
   c. They are come?
   d. None of the above

3. I cleaned up and spilled my milk.
   a. I spilled my milk and then cleaned up.
   b. The milk cleaned up and spilled.
   c. I cleaned and spilled the milk.
   d. None of the above

4. My homework I did first.
   a. I did first my homework.
   b. I did my homework first.
   c. My first homework did.
   d. None of the above

5. She ate dinner, fixed the salad and had dessert.
   a. She fixed the salad, ate dinner, and had dessert.
   b. She had dessert, fixed salad and ate dinner.
   c. She ate dessert, had salad and fixed dinner.
   d. None of the above

Content Cluster: STUDY SKILLS

Objective: Students will identify words in alphabetical order.

Parent Tip: Knowledge of alphabetical order is essential to the use of dictionaries, encyclopedias, telephone books, indices, and other resource materials.

Which word comes first in alphabetical (A-B-C) order? Mark the word in each set that would come first.

1. a. might
    b. maybe
    c. meat
    d. none of the above

2. a. table
    b. talk
    c. tangerine
    d. none of the above

3. a. bed
    b. bean
    c. being
    d. none of the above

4. a. machine
    b. material
    c. match
    d. none of the above

5. a. apple
    b. angle
    c. angel
    d. none of the above

6. a. catch
    b. caught
    c. calculate
    d. none of the above

7. a. funny
    b. funniest
    c. funnier
    d. none of the above

Content Cluster: VOCABULARY CONTRACTIONS

Objective: Students will identify a contraction, the shortened form of two words using an apostrophe.

Parent Tip: A contraction is two words joined together with one or more letters dropped and replaced by an apostrophe ('). Do not = don't   I will = I'll

---

ACTIVITY

Write the contraction. Read the word.

a. I will _____ do not _____

b. Will not_____ he is _____

c. I am _____ here is _____

Underline the contraction in each sentence below.

a. You'll enjoy the game.
b. I can't wait to go home.
c. Here's the book.
d. Isn't this a fun party?

CONTRACTIONS

Hint: when the word would is used in a contraction, the letters woul are dropped and replaced with an apostrophe (').
    I would – I'd   She would = she'd

ACTIVITY

Draw a line to match each pair of words with its contraction.

a. she would   you'd
b. he would   she'd
c. I would   they'd
d. who would   he'd
e. we would   we'd
f. they would   who'd
g. you would   I'd

Choose the correct contraction for each pair of words.

1. that is
   a. they're
   b. she'll
   c. that's
   d. none of the above

2. We had
   a. We've
   b. We'd
   c. We're
   d. None of the above

3. they will
   a. they'll
   b. they're
   c. they've
   d. none of the above

4. will not
   a. we've
   b. won't
   c. isn't
   d. none of the above

5. you are
   a. you're
   b. you'll
   c. you'd
   d. none of the above

6. here is
   a. he's
   b. here's
   c. she'd
   d. none of the above

7. do not
   a. don't
   b. does
   c. didn't
   d. none of the above

Content Cluster: SPELLING

Objective: Students will correctly spell frequently used and irregular words (e.g., was, were, says, said, who, what, why). They will spell basic short-vowel long-vowel, r-controlled, and consonant-blend patterns correctly.

Parent Tip: Encourage students to look carefully at the word, read the word, and take a best guess if still uncertain how the word should be spelled.

SPELLING ACTIVITY #1

The farmer grows many foods on his farm. Unscramble each word to find the correct answer.

1. asenb   _____
2. rnco   _____
3. espa   _____
4. pplaes   _____
5. hwtea   _____
6. racrtos _____
7. noions   _____
8. sqsuah   _____

SPELLING ACTIVITY #2

Put each group of words in alphabetical order.

snow _____   club _____

snail _____   clear _____

snug _____   clown _____

sneeze _____   clay _____

brake _____   drop _____

broke _____   drug _____

bring _____   dragon _____

broom _____   drive _____

SPELLING ACTIVITY #3

Rearrange the <u>underlined</u> letters of each word so it fits the clue for the new word you spelled.

1. <u>late</u> - a story   _____

2. <u>net</u> – the number of dimes in a dollar   _____

3. <u>nmae</u> – a horse has this on its head and neck   _____

4. <u>seat</u> – a direction   _____

5. <u>pan</u> - something you take when you're tired   _____

SPELLING ACTIVITY #4 – NOUN PLURALS (more than one)

Add e, es, s, or ies to the following words to make them plural words.

fish   _____

wish   _____

pass   _____

lunch   _____

fox   _____

dress   _____

lamp   _____

plant   _____

tray   _____

nest   _____

pinch   _____

splash   _____

watch   _____

window   _____

crash   _____

class   _____

SPELLING TEST # 1

Read each group of words. Mark the one that is <u>not</u> spelled correctly.

1. a. horse
    b. deare
    c. eight
    d. five

2. a. chain
    b. boat
    c. clap
    d. clas

3. a. drink
    b. onle
    c. late
    d. put

4. a. becuse
    b. turtle
    c. toy
    d. into

5. a. none
    b. noon
    c. trik
    d. truck

6. a. pensil
    b. playground
    c. note
    d. egg

7. a. won
    b. large
    c. elefant
    d. soft

8. a. mountan
    b. give
    c. print
    d. such

9. a. nine
    b. nice
    c. untill
    d. shell

10. a. sock
    b. ghost
    c. chirp
    d. brothr

11. a. eaten
    b. allso
    c. soup
    d. notice

12. a. aroind
    b. dinner
    c. finish
    d. below

13. a. snake
    b. voyce
    c. herself
    d. top

14. a. mask
    b. gaint
    c. choose
    d. built

15. a. pretind
    b. pay
    c. roll
    d. never

16. a. lake
    b. raine
    c. white
    d. read

17. a. apple
    b. papper
    c. star
    d. stand

SPELLING TEST #2

Find the word that best fits the sentence and is spelled correctly.

1. I won't _____ my dog.
    a. bothur
    b. bother
    c. bothir
    d. none of the above

2. I can do a _____.
    a. trick
    b. tric
    c. treck
    d. none of the above

3. My hair has _____ in it.
    a. cerl
    b. curl
    c. kurl
    d. none of the above

4. She has a phone _____.
    a. numbir
    b. number
    c. numbeer
    d. none of the above

5. My dog is _____.
    a. bron
    b. broun
    c. brown
    d. browne

6. The _____ is near the road.
    a. hospetol
    b. hospitle
    c. hospital
    d. haspital

7. He can _____ the ladder.
    a. climb
    b. clime
    c. climme
    d. climbe

SPELLING TEST #3

Read the sentences. Look for the word with the spelling mistake.

1. The teacher sez we are good students.
   a. teacher
   b. sez
   c. good
   d. students

2. She filt bad about the lost dog.
   a. filt
   b. about
   c. lost
   d. dog

3. I have to go strait home from school.
   a. strait
   b. home
   c. from
   d. school

4. I think I can get a stare on the spelling test.
   a. think
   b. stare
   c. spelling
   d. test

5. The childrun are playing outside on Tuesday.
   a. childrun
   b. playing
   c. outside
   d. Tuesday

SPELLING TEST #4

Find the word that best fits the sentence and is spelled correctly.

1. When did you _____?
   a. reterrn
   b. retirn
   c. return
   d. retern

2. What is the _____?
   a. anser
   b. answer
   c. ansur
   d. ansar

3. You gave me a _____ of the letter.
   a. kopy
   b. cope
   c. copy
   d. copie

4. The clown made me _____.
   a. laugh
   b. laff
   c. laf
   d. lauf

5. It is a pretty _____.
   a. berd
   b. bird
   c. burd
   d. bard

6. The _____ was in the water.
   a. bot
   b. bote
   c. boat
   d. bottle

7. You can plan _____.
   a. togethher
   b. togather
   c. together
   d. togethir

8. Your socks don't _____.
   a. madch
   b. mach
   c. mache
   d. match

9. This is my _____ place.
   a. favrit
   b. favrite
   c. favorite
   d. favorit

10. _____homes have people living in them.
    a. Both
    b. Boath
    c. Bothe
    d. Bouth

11. We saw the Grand Canyon _____.
    a. onse
    b. wunce
    c. once
    d. wonce

12. School starts _____.
    a. irly
    b. early
    c. urly
    d. erly

13. The ducks walked in a _____line.
    a. strate
    b. strayt
    c. straight
    d. strayght

14. My _____ is five years old.
    a. son
    b. sun
    c. sonn
    d. sone

Content Cluster: CAPITALIZATION

Objective: Students will capitalize all proper nouns, words at the beginning of sentences and greetings, months, days of the week, and titles and initials of people.

> **Parent Tip:** As students read each sentence, attention should focus on words needing capital letters.

Read the sentences. Circle the capitalization mistakes. Can you find all of them? Once you have, rewrite the sentences correctly.

1. i Go to school in caLiforNia.
2. mRs. SMith is the Name of my Teacher.
3. WE are starTing School in sepTemBer.
4. sHE is Going to neW yorK on SunDay.
5. he is a player for the los angeLes doDgers.

Corrected Sentences

1. I go to school in California.
2. Mrs. Smith is the name of my teacher.
3. We are starting school in September.
4. She is going to New York on Sunday.
5. He is a player for the Los Angeles Dodgers.

Choose the sentence that shows correct capitalization.

1. The game is on _____.
   a. Saturday Morning.
   b. saturday morning.
   c. Saturday morning.
   d. None of the above.

2. My _____ cooking dinner.
   a. Mother is
   b. mother is
   c. Mother is
   d. None of the above

3. I go to _____ .
   a. abraham Lincoln school.
   b. Abraham Lincoln school.
   c. Abraham Lincoln School.
   d. None of the above

Let's write a note! Fill in the blanks to write a letter to your teacher.

April 1, _____

Dear _____,

      Thank you for teaching me about _____. I will tell my friend about _____. I am happy you are my _____ grade teacher.

Sincerely,

_____

Mark the answer that shows correct capitalization. Read each sentence carefully. There is only one sentence that is correct.

1. a. Which Dog belongs to you
     b. I will go to Boston to get one.
     c. We might have to go to the Office.
     d. do you thing it will be fun?

2. a. We can play Ball at the park.
     b. mike said that we can play together
     c. I want to try and play baseball.
     d. Do you think i can do it?

3. a. We like to eat hamburgers on saturday.
     b. She will go to Foothill Street.
     c. They will try to Read the menu.
     d. I know i can eat ice cream, too.

Content Cluster: SYNONYMS

Objective: Students will identify words that have the same meaning.

Parent Tip: Encourage students to skip difficult items and return to them later.

Read each item carefully. Find the word that means the same or almost the same as the <u>underlined</u> word.

1. <u>large</u> flowers
   a. colored
   b. pretty
   c. big
   d. small

2. <u>rear</u> of the car
   a. wheel
   b. window
   c. side
   d. back

3. <u>happy</u> birthday
   a. cheerful
   b. busy
   c. cake
   d. balloons

4. <u>small</u> cookie
   a. chocolate
   b. tiny
   c. striped
   d. filled

5. <u>sad</u> boy
   a. silly
   b. bold
   c. old
   d. unhappy

6. look <u>beneath</u>
   a. beside
   b. below
   c. above
   d. along

7. <u>free</u> the animal
   a. harm
   b. attract
   c. release
   d. search

8. <u>View</u> the movie
   a. watch
   b. leave
   c. enjoy
   d. laugh

9. Go to the <u>back</u> of the bus.
   a. side
   b. inside
   c. front
   d. rear

10. The kite is <u>high</u> in the sky.
    a. far
    b. up
    c. along
    d. beyond

Content Cluster: ANTONYMS

Objective: Students will identify words with opposite meanings.

Parent Tip: Ask student which of four words is opposite of the underlined word.

Read each item carefully. Find the word that means the opposite of the underlined word.

1. <u>toss</u> the ball
   a. throw
   b. catch
   c. find
   d. hit

2. <u>some</u> candy
   a. seven
   b. several
   c. no
   d. that

3. work <u>slowly</u>
   a. rapidly
   b. soon
   c. some
   d. kindly

4. <u>angry</u> child
   a. curious
   b. happy
   c. sad
   d. calm

5. the <u>woman</u>
   a. baby
   b. child
   c. man
   d. boy

6. <u>crying</u> baby
    a. sleeping
    b. laughing
    c. playing
    d. jumping

7. <u>tall</u> man
    a. short
    b. fat
    c. small
    d. long

8. <u>sick</u> boy
    a. happy
    b. sad
    c. well
    d. cold

9. running <u>quickly</u>
    a. slowly
    b. quietly
    c. rapidly
    d. playfully

10. <u>recent</u> newspaper
    a. old
    b. cheat
    c. expensive
    d. thick

Content Cluster: WORD ANALYSIS

Objective: Students will identify phonemes.

Parent Tip: Emphasize the underlined sound in each word and carefully look at the beginning, middle, and end of each word choice for that same sound. Think of other words with the same <u>sounds</u> and list them.

One or more letters are underlined in each of the words below. Read each word, then choose the correct word that has the same sound as the underlined letter or letters.

1. <u>bl</u>ame
    a. problem
    b. ball
    c. balloon
    d. none of the above

2. <u>sl</u>eep
    a. salt
    b. slim
    c. sail
    d. none of the above

3. <u>v</u>iolet
    a. November
    b. Blue
    c. Orange
    d. None of the above

4. <u>th</u>umb
    a. trace
    b. both
    c. toe
    d. none of the above

5. <u>st</u>eam
    a. say
    b. stay
    c. team
    d. none of the above

6. chil<u>dr</u>en
   a. dirt
   b. harm
   c. draw
   d. none of the above

7. mu<u>st</u>
   a. fish
   b. stand
   c. with
   d. none of the above

8. gra<u>nd</u>
   a. faint
   b. plant
   c. stand
   d. none of the above

9. bl<u>ue</u>
   a. they
   b. chest
   c. bend
   d. crew

10. l<u>ea</u>f
    a. red
    b. keep
    c. kept
    d. bread

11. st<u>iff</u>
    a. wig
    b. like
    c. life
    d. drive

12. r<u>u</u>de
    a. mud
    b. coat
    c. loop
    d. chore

13. b<u>ea</u>ch
    a. see
    b. touch
    c. dead
    d. made

14. b<u>oi</u>l
    a. boss
    b. toy
    c. toad
    d. mate

15. ch<u>ur</u>ch
    a. torn
    b. bird
    c. tune
    d. moon

16. m<u>a</u>de
    a. mad
    b. lap
    c. may
    d. read

17. d<u>ai</u>sy
    a. boat
    b. stay
    c. moat
    d. boat

18. r<u>ea</u>d
    a. draw
    b. stripe
    c. seed
    d. ride

ANSWER KEY

Reading Comprehension

Activity
1. c
2. b
3. d

Test #1
1. c
2. c
3. a

Activity #1
1. b
2. a
3. c
4. b
5. b

Activity #2
1. d
2. c
3. b
4. b
5. c

Activity #3
1. b
2. d
3. c
4. c
5. c

Activity #4
1. b
2. a
3. c
4. b
5. a

Activity #5
1. c
2. b
3. c
4. a
5. c

Textual
Activity #1
1. c
2. b
3. c
4. d
5. a
6. b
7. a
8. c

Activity #2
1. c
2. c
3. a
4. b
5. b

Activity #3
1. c
2. a
3. b
4. d
5. a

Recreational
1. c
2. b
3. a
4. b
5. c
6. a
7. b
8. d
9. b
10. a

Functional
1. c
2. b
3. c
4. a
5. c
6. c
7. a

Cause and Effect
1. b
2. a
3. c
4. a
5. b
6. a
7. b
8. c
9. a
10. b

Reading Vocabulary
1. c
2. b
3. c
4. c
5. c
6. a
7. c
8. a
9. b
10. c

Capitalization
1. b
2. d
3. b
4. c
5. b
6. b
7. a

Punctuation
1. a
2. b
3. c
4. a
5. b
6. c
7. c
8. c
9. b
10. a

Usage
1. b
2. a
3. c
4. c
5. a
6. b
7. a
8. a
9. b
10. a

Sentence Structure and Content Organization
1. a
2. b
3. a
4. b
5. a

Study Skills
1. b
2. a
3. b
4. a
5. c
6. c
7. c

Vocabulary Contractions
a. I'll don't
b. Won't he's
c. I'm here's
d. You'll
e. can't
f. Here's
g. Isn't

Contractions
she'd
he'd
I'd
who'd
we'd
they'd
you'd

Test
1. c
2. b
3. a
4. b
5. a
6. b
7. a

Spelling Activity #1
1. beans
2. corn
3. peas
4. apples
5. wheat
6. carrots
7. onions
8. squash

Spelling Activity #2
snail
sneeze
snow
snug
clay
clear
clown
club
brake
bring
broke
broom
dragon
drive
drop
drug

Spelling Activity #3
tale
ten
mane
east
nap

Spelling Activity #4
fishes
wishes
passes
lunches
foxes
dresses
lamps
plants
trays
nests
pinches
splashes
watches
windows
crashes
classes

Spelling Test #1
1. b
2. d
3. b
4. a
5. c
6. a
7. c
8. a
9. c
10. d
11. b
12. a
13. b
14. b
15. a
16. b
17. b

Spelling Test #2
1. b
2. a
3. b
4. b
5. c
6. c
7. a

Spelling Test #3
1. b
2. a
3. a
4. b
5. a

Spelling Test #4
1. c
2. b
3. c
4. a
5. b
6. c
7. c
8. d
9. c
10. a
11. c
12. b
13. c
14. a

Capitalization
1. c
2. b
3. c

1. b
2. c
3. b

Synonyms
1. c
2. d
3. a
4. b
5. d
6. b
7. c
8. a
9. d
10. b

Antonyms
1. b
2. c
3. a
4. b
5. c
6. b
7. a
8. c
9. a
10. a

Word Analysis
1. a
2. b
3. a
4. b
5. b
6. c
7. b
8. c
9. d
10. b
11. a
12. c
13. a
14. b
15. b
16. c
17. b
18. c

MATH

Content Cluster: ADDITION

Objective: Students will solve problems using addition.

Parent Tip: When students recopy problems on scratch paper, make sure they line up the numbers correctly.

Solve the following problems and choose the correct answer.

1. $7 + 2 =$

    a. 3
    b. 8
    c. 9
    d. 5

2. $6 + 4 =$

    a. 7
    b. 10
    c. 9
    d. 11

3. $6 + 5 =$

    a. 11
    b. 12
    c. 13
    d. 14

4. $86 + 16 =$

    a. 92
    b. 112
    c. 102
    d. 122

5. 9 + 3 =

    a. 12
    b. 15
    c. 11
    d. 13

6. 22 + 45 + 10 =

    a. 65
    b. 67
    c. 77
    d. 57

7. 276 + 664 =

    a. 830
    b. 940
    c. 834
    d. 944

8. 6 + 2 + 8 =

    a. 16
    b. 12
    c. 14
    d. 24

9. 5035 + 3921 =

    a. 7946
    b. 8856
    c. 7955
    d. 8956

10. 51 + 5 =

    a. 101
    b. 65
    c. 56
    d. 11

11. $90 + 60 =$

    a. 130
    b. 140
    c. 150
    d. 135

12. $26 + 6 =$

    a. 32
    b. 212
    c. 206
    d. 23

13. $5 + 4 =$

    a. 8
    b. 9
    c. 11
    d. 12

14. $35 + 14 =$

    a. 58
    b. 59
    c. 49
    d. 76

15. $7 + 8 =$

    a. 16
    b. 87
    c. 15
    d. 12

16. $97 + 27 =$

    a. 162
    b. 116
    c. 114
    d. 124

Content Cluster: SUBTRACTION

Objective: Students will solve problems using subtraction.

Parent Tip: When students recopy problems on scratch paper, make sure they line up the numbers correctly. It is important for them to practice the skill of copying and calculating the problem, because there is no writing allowed in the actual test booklet.

Solve the following problems and choose the correct answer.

1. $83 - 61 =$

    a. 51
    b. 42
    c. 32
    d. 22

2. $62 - 7 =$

    a. 45
    b. 55
    c. 47
    d. 52

3. $446 - 33 =$

    a. 443
    b. 313
    c. 416
    d. 413

4. $50 - 7 =$

    a. 57
    b. 46
    c. 43
    d. 52

5. $60 - 5 =$

    a. 65
    b. 52
    c. 55
    d. 45

6. 97 – 18 =

    a. 79
    b. 89
    c. 88
    d. 76

7. 25 – 9 =

    a. 25
    b. 26
    c. 27
    d. 16

8. 823 – 5 =

    a. 718
    b. 818
    c. 822
    d. 723

9. 83 – 7 =

    a. 66
    b. 84
    c. 73
    d. 76

10. 17 – 9 =

    a. 12
    b. 8
    c. 16
    d. 9

11. 68 – 66

    a. 62
    b. 6
    c. 2
    d. 61

12. 59 – 4 =

    a. 55
    b. 54
    c. 44
    d. 48

13. 14 – 2 =

    a. 12
    b. 14
    c. 13
    d. 11

14. 13 – 6 =

    a. 4
    b. 5
    c. 7
    d. 6

15. 9 – 4 =

    a. 3
    b. 13
    c. 7
    d. 5

16. 13 – 7 =

    a. 11
    b. 9
    c. 6
    d. 7

17. 76 – 73 =

    a. 3
    b. 13
    c. 2
    d. 12

Content Cluster: MULTIPLICATION

Objective: Students will solve simple multiplication problems.

> **Parent Tip:** Use drawings to illustrate how many groups are being multiplied how many times. Recognize that multiplication is repeated addition.

Solve the following problems and choose the correct answer.

1. 2 x 1 =

   a. 1
   b. 3
   c. 4
   d. 2

2. 5 x 6 =

   a. 11
   b. 35
   c. 30
   d. 20

3. 10 x 5 =

   a. 50
   b. 15
   c. 40
   d. 150

4. 3 x 3 =

   a. 12
   b. 6
   c. 9
   d. 15

5. 4 x 3 =
   a. 12
   b. 13
   c. 7
   d. 8

6. 5 x 5 =

    a. 15
    b. 10
    c. 25
    d. 20

7. 7 x 2 =

    a. 9
    b. 16
    c. 6
    d. 14

8. 10 x 7 =

    a. 60
    b. 17
    c. 70
    d. 80

9. 8 x 2 =

    a. 16
    b. 10
    c. 12
    d. 16

10. 5 x 7 =

    a. 30
    b. 35
    c. 40
    d. 45

Content Cluster: DIVISION

Objective: Students will solve simple division problems.

Parent Tip: Use drawings to illustrate how many items can be divided into how many groups.

Solve the following problems and choose the correct answer.

1. $33 \div 3 =$

    a. 22
    b. 11
    c. 99
    d. 12

2. $9 \div 3 =$

    a. 2
    b. 6
    c. 12
    d. 3

3. $8 \div 2 =$

    a. 6
    b. 4
    c. 8
    d. 10

4. $80 \div 4 =$

    a. 20
    b. 24
    c. 40
    d. 50

5. $46 \div 2 =$

    a. 23
    b. 14
    c. 81
    d. 32

6. $25 \div 5 =$

    a. 20
    b. 5
    c. 4
    d. 2

7. $18 \div 3 =$

    a. 2
    b. 25
    c. 7
    d. 6

8. $40 \div 5 =$

    a. 20
    b. 8
    c. 10
    d. 30

Content Cluster: PROBLEM SOLVING –
Number Sense & Numeration

Objective: Students will understand the relationship among numbers, quantities, and place value in whole numbers to 1000.

Parent Tip: Students must carefully check and recheck answer before marking.

Look at the number in bold type and the answer choices.

1. **432**   Choose the numeral that is in the hundreds place.

   a. 4
   b. 3
   c. 2
   d. 400

2. **712**   Choose the numeral that is in the tens place.

   a. 7
   b. 2
   c. 1
   d. 12

3. **25**   Choose the numeral that is in the ones place.

   a. 2
   b. 5
   c. 0
   d. 25

4. **659**   Choose the numeral that is in the hundreds place.

   a. 5
   b. 9
   c. 6
   d. 59

5. **105**   Choose the numeral in the tens place.

   a. 1
   b. 5
   c. 10
   d. 0

1. 4 tens 6 ones =

   a. 46
   b. 406
   c. 64
   d. 604

2. 3 tens 9 ones =

   a. 93
   b. 309
   c. 39
   d. 339

3. 27 =

   a. 7 tens
   b. 27 ones
   c. 72 ones
   d. 72 tens

4. 439 =

   a. 42 hundreds, 9 tens
   b. 4 hundreds, 3 tens, 9 ones
   c. 4 tens, 3 hundreds, 9 ones
   d. 4 ones, 3 tens, 9 ones

5. Which numeral stands for sixteenth?

   a. 60
   b. 600
   c. 16
   d. 61

6. Which is an <u>even</u> number?

   a. 23
   b. 35
   c. 17
   d. 16

7. Which number is greater than 2 and less than 6?

   a. 7
   b. 2
   c. 6
   d. 3

8. Which number belongs in the box?   10, ☐ , 30, 40, 50

   a. 12
   b. 20
   c. 30
   d. 40

9. Which number belongs in the box?   20, 40, ☐ , 80, 100

   a. 30
   b. 50
   c. 60
   d. 70

10. Which number has a 5 in the hundreds place?

   a. 1075
   b. 5062
   c. 8543
   d. 7453

11. Which is the odd number?

   a. 13
   b. 24
   c. 38
   d. 54

Content Cluster: PROBLEM SOLVING –
Geometry and Spatial Sense

Objective: Students can describe and classify plane and solid geometric shapes according to the number and shape of faces, edges and vertices. (Circle, triangle, square, rectangle, sphere, pyramid, cube, rectangular prism)

Parent Tip: The student should put shapes together and take them apart to form other shapes. They will understand the concept of symmetry without necessarily using the word symmetry.

Answer the following questions.

1. Which circle has 2 parts that are exactly the same?

a. 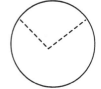   b.   c.   d.

2. What shapes are in this picture?

    a. two triangles and 1 square
    b. 2 squares and 2 triangles
    c. 1 rectangle and 2 squares
    d. 2 triangles and 2 rectangles

3. How many sides does a square have?

    a. 3
    b. 2
    c. 5
    d. 4

4. How many sides does a triangle have?

    a. 3
    b. 4
    c. 2
    d. 5

5. Which object is cut into two equal pieces?

a.   b.   c.   d.

6. Which figure contains 2 squares?

a.   b   c.   d.

7. Which item contains a pair of triangles?

a.   b.   c.   d.

8. Which figure is a cylinder?

a.   b.   c.   d.

9. Which figure is a cube?

a.   b.   c.   d.

10. Which coordinate gives the location of the star?

a. B 3
b. E 4
c. D 3
d. D 2

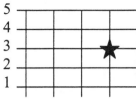

11. Which coordinate gives the location of the star?

a. C 4
b. B 4
c. D 4
d. A 5

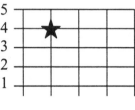

12. Which coordinate gives the location of the star?

a. E 1
b. C 2
c. A 1
d. D 5

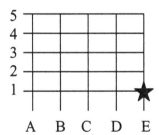

Content Cluster: PROBLEM SOLVING –
Measurement

Objective: Students will understand that measurement is accomplished by identifying a unit of measure, repeating that unit, and comparing it to the item to be measured. Students will measure using inches or centimeters. Students will tell time to the nearest quarter hour and know the time relationships. Students will determine the duration of time intervals in hours.

Parent Tip: Practice measuring items with appropriate rulers and telling time on a clock with minute and hour hands.

Answer the following questions.

1. How long is the pencil?

    a. 2 centimeters
    b. 3 centimeters
    c. 4 centimeters
    d. 6 centimeters

2. How long is the eraser?

    a. 1 inch
    b. 2 inches
    c. 3 inches
    d. ½ inch

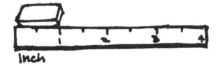

3. Which clock says 12:30?

a.  b. 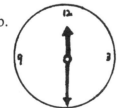 c.  d.

4. Which clock says 6:00?

a. 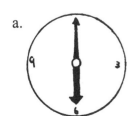 b.  c.  d.

5. Which clock says 3:45?

a.    b. 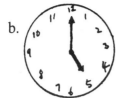   c. 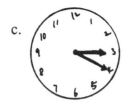   d.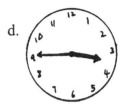

6. How many hours pass between 10:00AM and 4:00PM?

    a. 6 hours
    b. 4 hours
    c. 14 hours
    d. 7 hours

7. How many hours pass between 9:00PM and 7:00AM?

    a. 9 hours
    b. 7 hours
    c. 10 hours
    d. 8 hours

8. Which sentence is true?

    a. 1 foot = 21 inches
    b. 1 foot = 36 inches
    c. 1 foot = 12 inches
    d. 1 foot = 1 inch

9. What is the temperature shown on this thermometer?

    a. 20°
    b. 22°
    c. 21°
    d. 26°

10. What would be the best measurement to use for identifying your weight?

    a. inches
    b. miles
    c. pounds
    d. ounces

11. What unit of measure should the students use to weigh a box of cereal?

    a. centimeters
    b. pounds
    c. kilograms
    d. ounces

12. Which metric unit would you use to measure the distance from one town to another?

    a. kilogram
    b. kilometer
    c. meter
    d. gram

13. Which metric unit would you use to measure the weight of your big dog?

    a. kilogram
    b. kilometer
    c. meter
    d. gram

14. How many centimeters long is the toothbrush?

    a. 11
    b. 10
    c. 9
    d. 8

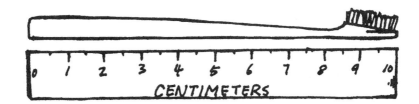

15. Mark the correct answer that matches the time on the clock.

    a. 9:06
    b. 5:45
    c. 6:15
    d. 9:30

MAY

Sun	Mon	Tues	Wed	Thurs	Fri	Sat
1	2	3	4	5	6	7
8	9	10	11	12	13	14
15	16	17	18	19	20	21
22	23	24	25	26	27	28
29	30	31				

16. How many Sundays in the above calendar of May?

    a. 8
    b. 4
    c. 5
    d. 1

17. What is the date of the second Tuesday?

    a. 2
    b. 30
    c. 24
    d. 10

18. What day is the 26th of May?

    a. Monday
    b. Wednesday
    c. Thursday
    d. Friday

Content Cluster: PROBLEM SOLVING –
Patterns and Relationships

Objective: Students will solve problems involving simple number patterns.

Parent Tip: Assist this activity by saying numerals in the pattern aloud to hear as well as see the pattern.

Look at the number patterns. Choose the correct answer that fits the empty box.

1. 22, ☐ , 26, 28

    a. 24
    b. 25
    c. 12
    d. 21

2. 33, 36, ☐ , 42

    a. 35
    b. 37
    c. 39
    d. 40

3. 1, 5, 9, ☐ , 17

    a. 13
    b. 15
    c. 16
    d. 10

4. ☐ , 14, 16, 18, 20

    a. 13
    b. 15
    c. 10
    d. 12

5. 30, 45, 60, ☐ , 90

    a. 70
    b. 75
    c. 80
    d. 89

Content Cluster: PROBLEM SOLVING –
Fractions

Objective: Students will understand that fractions can refer to parts of a set and parts of a whole. Students will recognize common fractions, compare unit fractions up to 1/12, and recognize fractions of a whole and parts of a group. (e.g., ¼ of a pie, 2/3 of 15 balls)

Parent Tip: Try cutting fruit into equal parts to see actual fractions in action.

Answer the following questions.

1. What fraction names the shaded part of the shape?

    a. 1/5
    b. 1/3
    c. 2/6
    d. 1/6

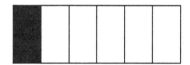

2. What fraction describes the shaded circles?

    a. 3/3
    b. 1/3
    c. 2/3
    d. 1/5

3. Which object is ¼ filled in?

a.   b.   c.   d.

4. What part is shaded?

    a. 2/4
    b. 1/3
    c. 2/5
    d. 2/3

5. What part is shaded?

   a. 2/4
   b. 1/3
   c. 2/5
   d. 2/3

6. What part is shaded?

   a. 2/4
   b. 1/3
   c. 3/4
   d. 2/3

7. What part is shaded?

   a. 2/4
   b. 1/3
   c. 2/5
   d. 2/3

8. What part is shaded?

   a. 2/4
   b. 1/3
   c. 2/5
   d. 6/9

9. What part is shaded?

   a. 2/3
   b. 2/5
   c. 3/5
   d. 1/5

10. What part is shaded?

    a. 2/3
    b. 2/5
    c. 3/5
    d. 4/8

Content Cluster: PROBLEM SOLVING –
Statistics and Probability

Objective: Students will perform correct operations using information from graphs.

Parent Tip: If the student needs to diagram or draw to help solve a problem, s/he should use scratch paper. He or she must be careful to transfer the correct answer from the scratch paper to the answer key.

Use the chart to answer the following questions.

Hair Color	Boy							Girl						
Blonde	■							■						
Lt Brown	■	■	■	■	■			■	■	■				
Dk Brown	■	■						■	■	■	■	■		
Red	■		■					■						
Black								■						
	1	2	3	4	5	6	7	1	2	3	4	5	6	7

1. How many girls have blonde hair?

   a. 4
   b. 7
   c. 2
   d. 1

2. How many more boys have light brown hair than girls that have light brown hair?

   a. 7
   b. 2
   c. 5
   d. 3

3. How many boys and girls have dark brown hair?

   a. 7
   b. 8
   c. 9
   d. 10

4. How many students are in the class?

    a. 30
    b. 29
    c. 28
    d. 15

5. Are there more students with light brown hair or dark brown hair in the class?

    a. light brown
    b. dark brown
    c. blonde
    d. red

6. Counting by ones, what number comes after 39?

    a. 38
    b. 29
    c. 40
    d. 41

7. How many tens are in 58?

    a. 8
    b. 5
    c. 4
    d. 6

8. How many of these numbers are less than 67? **78   59   69   47**

    a. 2
    b. 3
    c. 1
    d. 4

9. What symbol correctly completes the number sentence below?

$$16 \; \boxed{} \; 8 = 8$$

    a. +
    b. −
    c. x
    d. ÷

10. If you are the third person in line, which person is in front of you?

    a. fourth
    b. fifth
    c. second
    d. seventh

11. What will make the number sentences true?
$$\_\_\_\_ + 5 = 11 \qquad 11 - \_\_\_\_ = 5$$

    a. 15
    b. 16
    c. 7
    d. 6

12. There are 20 students in a class. Each student brought in 5 bugs for science. How can you find the number of insects they brought in all together?

    a. divide
    b. subtract
    c. multiply
    d. add

13. If you put these numbers in order, which would be the first?
127   172   107   117

    a. 127
    b. 172
    c. 107
    d. 117

14. Which number fits the blank to make it correct?
$$7 + 5 + 3 = \_\_\_\_$$

    a. 7
    b. 15
    c. 6
    d. 8

Use the numbers on the balls to write a three-digit-number.

1. What is the largest number that can be made?

    a. 236
    b. 623
    c. 632
    d. 326

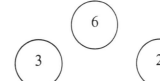

2. What is the smallest number that can be made with a 2 in the ones place?

    a. 623
    b. 236
    c. 362
    d. 326

3. What is the largest number that can be made with a 5 in the tens place?

    a. 954
    b. 945
    c. 595
    d. 459

4. What number is greater than 549 but less than 945?

    a. 954
    b. 594
    c. 459
    d. 495

Content Cluster: PROBLEM SOLVING –
Procedures

Objective: Students will read and solve simple mathematical situations.

Parent Tip: The student should remember key words when determining which procedure to use to solve a problem. Addition words – in all, altogether. Subtraction words – how many more, how many fewer, how many left.

Read each problem and choose the correct number sentence.

1. 18 boys went on a hike. 9 girls also went. How many more boys went hiking than girls?

   a. $18 + 9 = 27$ more boys
   b. $8 + 9 = 17$ more boys
   c. $18 - 9 = 9$ more boys
   d. none of the above

2. The students saw 15 birds in the morning and 6 in the afternoon. How many fewer birds did they see in the afternoon?

   a. $6 + 5 = 11$ birds
   b. $15 - 6 = 9$ birds
   c. $15 + 6 = 21$ birds
   d. none of the above

3. Mike saw 7 big fish. Lynn saw 6 small fish. How many fish did they see altogether?

   a. $7 + 6 = 13$ fish
   b. $7 - 6 = 1$ fish
   c. $7 + 6 + 3 = 16$ fish
   d. none of the above

4. Carrie picked 8 flowers. Anne picked 8 flowers. How many flowers did they have in all?

   a. $8 - 8 = 0$ flowers
   b. $8 + 8 = 16$ flowers
   c. $8 + 8 + 2 = 18$ flowers
   d. none of the above

5. Sally found 14 books. She gave 8 to Nancy. How many books did Sally have left?

    a. 4 + 8 = 12 books
    b. 14 − 8 = 6 books
    c. 14 + 8 = 22 books
    d. none of the above

Mark the correct amount that matches the coins.

1. a. 28¢
    b. 38¢
    c. 55¢
    d. none of the above

2. a. 78¢
    b. 79¢
    c. 80¢
    d. none of the above

3. a. 70¢
    b. 60¢
    c. 55¢
    d. none of the above

4. a. 39¢
    b. 49¢
    c. 50¢
    d. none of the above

5. a. 70¢
    b. 46¢
    c. 51¢
    d. none of the above

6. a. 27¢
    b. 35¢
    c. 56¢
    d. none of the above

7. a. 85¢
    b. 76¢
    c. 90¢
    d. none of the above

8. a. 60¢
    b. 45¢
    c. 55¢
    d. none of the above

9. a. 93¢
    b. 83¢
    c. 78¢
    d. none of the above

10. a. 30¢
    b. 50¢
    c. 60¢
    d. none of the above

11. a. 85¢
    b. 75¢
    c. 60¢
    d. none of the above

12. a. 53¢
    b. 38¢
    c. 63¢
    d. none of the above

13. a. 60¢
    b. 37¢
    c. 75¢
    d. none of the above

14. a. 34¢
    b. 24¢
    c. 22¢
    d. none of the above

Math Time – Mark the answer that matches the time on the clock

1. a. 2:15
    b. 3:15
    c. 2:00
    d. none of the above

2. a. 12:00
    b. 1:00
    c. 11:00
    d. none of the above

3. a. 9:45
    b. 9:00
    c. 8:45
    d. none of the above

4. a. 6:30
    b. 5:30
    c. 4:30
    d. none of the above

5. a. 4:45
    b. 4:15
    c. 3:45
    d. none of the above

6. a. 6:00
    b. 11:00
    c. 11:30
    d. none of the above

7. a. 7:15
    b. 3:00
    c. 9:00
    d. none of the above

Content Cluster: PROBLEM SOLVING –
Graphing

Objective: Students will read graphs and analyze information.

Parent Tip: Remind students to carefully review the information provided on the side, top or bottom of graphs.

Use the graph to answer the following questions.

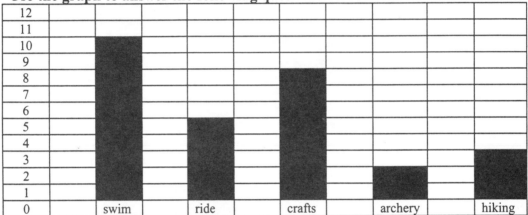

1. How many children went swimming?
   a. 8
   b. 10
   c. 2
   d. 6

2. How many children went hiking?
   a. 3
   b. 9
   c. 4
   d. 7

3. What was picked by the most children?
   a. swimming
   b. crafts
   c. ride
   d. archery

4. What was picked by the fewest children?
   a. hiking
   b. crafts
   c. swimming
   d. archery

Use the graph to answer the following questions.

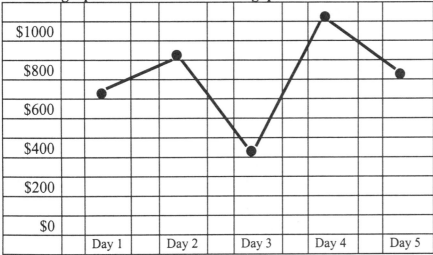

Come to a 5 Day Toy Sale!

1. How much money was spent on toys on day 3?
   a. $400
   b. $200
   c. $300
   d. $100

2. How much money was spent on day 1?
   a. $600
   b. $700
   c. $800
   d. $900

3. How much money was spent on day 5?
   a. $600
   b. $700
   c. $800
   d. $900

4. On what day was the greatest amount sold?
   a. day 5
   b. day 4
   c. day 2
   d. day 1

5. On what day was the smallest amount sold?
   a. day 3
   b. day 5
   c. day 1
   d. day 4

ANSWER KEY

MATH

Addition
1. c
2. b
3. a
4. c
5. a
6. c
7. b
8. a
9. d
10. c
11. c
12. a
13. b
14. c
15. c
16. d

Subtraction
1. d
2. b
3. d
4. c
5. c
6. a
7. d
8. b
9. d
10. b
11. c
12. a
13. a
14. c
15. d
16. c
17. a

Multiplication
1. d
2. c
3. a

4. c
5. a
6. c
7. d
8. c
9. a
10. b

Division
1. b
2. d
3. b
4. a
5. a
6. b
7. d
8. b

Problem Solving & Number Sense
1. a
2. c
3. b
4. c
5. d

1. a
2. c
3. b
4. b
5. c
6. d
7. d
8. b
9. c
10. c
11. a

Geometry and Spatial Sense
1. c
2. d

3. d
4. a
5. c
6. b
7. c
8. d
9. b
10. c
11. b
12. a

Measurement
1. c
2. a
3. b
4. a
5. d
6. a
7. c
8. c
9. a
10. c
11. d
12. b
13. a
14. b
15. b
16. c
17. d
18. c

Patterns and Relationships
1. a
2. c
3. a
4. d
5. b

Fractions
1. d
2. c
3. b

4. a
5. d
6. c
7. b
8. d
9. b
10. d

Statistics and Probability
1. c
2. b
3. d
4. b
5. a
6. c
7. b
8. a
9. b
10. c
11. d
12. c
13. c
14. b

1. c
2. c
3. a
4. b

Procedures
1. c
2. b
3. a
4. b
5. b

Coins
1. a
2. b
3. c
4. a
5. b

6. c
7. a
8. c
9. a
10. b
11. a
12. c
13. b
14. c

Time
1. a
2. a
3. c
4. b
5. c
6. c
7. a

Graphing
1. b
2. a
3. a
4. d

1. a
2. b
3. c
4. b
5. a

SCIENCE

Content Cluster: PHYSICAL SCIENCE

Objective: Students will know that the motion of objects can be observed and measured.

Parent Tips: According to the California State Science Content Standards:
- The way to change how something moves is to give it a push or a pull. The size of the change is related to the strength, or the amount of "force," of the push or pull.
- Tools and machines can be used to push or pull (forces) to make things move.
- Objects near the Earth fall to the ground unless something holds them up.
- Magnets can be used to make some objects move without being touched.
- Sound is made by vibrating objects and can be described by its pitch and volume.

Magnets

A magnet is an object that contains metal and attracts some other metals. Natural magnets are found in rocks. They have different shapes and sizes. People can make magnets, too. There are bar magnets, horseshoe magnets, and even magnets shaped like doughnuts. The core of the Earth is a big magnet.

Magnets are made of tiny pieces called molecules. These molecules are much smaller than even a speck of dust. You cannot even see them with your eyes alone. In most objects, molecules are scattered in different directions. When molecules are scattered, they are not magnetized and do not attract other objects.

In a magnet, all molecules face the same direction. When molecules face the same direction, they are magnetized. They will attract some other metal objects like coins, keys and paper clips. These usually contain iron.

These molecules are like rowers in a rowboat. If they push or pull their oars in every direction, the boat won't move. When the rowers face the same direction and pull their oars at the same time, the boat will move forward. The molecules in magnets work in a similar way.

1. Magnets provide
   a. push and pull power
   b. light power
   c. water pressure
   d. none of the above

2. A magnet can attract
   a. plastic
   b. glass
   c. some metals
   d. rubber

3. Magnets can be found in
   a. paper
   b. rocks
   c. cards
   d. wood

4. People make magnets that can be shaped like
   a. horseshoes
   b. apples
   c. boats
   d. cars

5. Magnets are made of tiny
   a. raindrops
   b. molecules
   c. plastic
   d. pieces of glass

6. A magnet can pull a
   a. potato
   b. paper bag
   c. coin
   d. chair

7. What part of the earth is a big magnet?
   a. the crust
   b. the core
   c. the mantle
   d. the sky

Content Cluster: LIFE SCIENCE

Objective: Students will know that organisms reproduce offspring of their own. The sequential stages of life cycles are different for different animals. The germination of plants can be affected by light, gravity, touch, or environmental stress. Flowers and fruits in plants are associated with reproduction. Students will understand the life cycles of organisms such as butterflies and frogs.

Parent Tip: Read a variety of nonfiction selections with the student to enhance comprehension of this science standard.

Answer the following questions by choosing the correct answer.

1. A butterfly begins life as a(n) _____

   a. worm
   b. fly
   c. egg
   d. cocoon

2. A <u>larva</u> is called a _____.

   a. butterfly
   b. caterpillar
   c. worm
   d. egg

3. When the caterpillar is fully-grown, it sheds its skin and becomes a <u>pupa</u>. It is covered with a hard shell called a <u>chrysalis</u> and changes into a _____.

   a. butterfly
   b. worm
   c. egg
   d. fly

4. The study of plants is called _____.

   a. botany
   b. biology
   c. paleontology
   d. geography

5. All plants have roots. Roots grow down into the soil and _____.

    a. take in water
    b. provide flowers
    c. grow leaves
    d. shrink

6. Leaves produce _____ for the plant.

    a. flowers
    b. roots
    c. food
    d. dirt

7. Leaves contain a green substance called _____.

    a. chlorophyll
    b. sweetgum
    c. palm
    d. none of the above

8. The stem of a plant _____.

    a. takes in sun
    b. carries food to the parts of the plant
    c. provides color
    d. none of the above

9. We can eat the leaves of some plants. What plant do we eat leaves from?

    a. roses
    b. grass
    c. lettuce
    d. dirt

10. We eat some plant roots. What plant do we eat that is a root?

    a. apple tree
    b. carrot
    c. strawberry
    d. orange

Content Cluster: EARTH SCIENCE

Objective: Students will compare physical properties of different kinds of rocks and know that rocks are composed of different combinations of minerals. Smaller rocks come from the weathering and breakage of larger rocks.

Parent Tip: Read all about how rocks are formed. Work with your child to answer any of the difficult questions that arise.

A Few Facts...

- Fossils provide evidence about the plants and animals that lived long ago.
- Rock, water, plants, and soil provide many resources including food, fuel, and building materials we use.
- Melted rock called magma is deep within the earth. When magma comes up through openings in the Earth's crust, it is called lava. Lava cools to form hard <u>igneous</u> rocks. The deepest part of the Earth is called the core. The mantle is the first layer below the crust.
- Wind and water break rocks into smaller pieces. The small pieces settle at the bottom of rivers and oceans. These layers of sediment harden to form sedimentary rocks.
- Heat and pressure deep within the Earth can cause igneous and sedimentary rocks to change. Rocks that are changed are called meta<u>morphic</u>.

Read the questions and choose the correct answer.

1. _____ cools to form hard igneous rocks.

    a. Rivers
    b. Lava
    c. Leaves
    d. Water

2. _____ rock is called magma.

    a. Melted rock
    b. Red rock
    c. River
    d. None of the above

3. Water and wind break rocks into small _____.

   a. seeds
   b. pieces
   c. plants
   d. none of the above

4. Rocks that are _____ are called metamorphic.

   a. lava
   b. orange
   c. changed
   d. none of the above

5. Layers of sediment _____ to form sedimentary rocks.

   a. travel
   b. harden
   c. melt
   d. none of the above

6. The deepest part of the Earth is the _____.

   a. core
   b. mantle
   c. crust
   d. edge

7. The layer under the Earth's crust is called the _____.

   a. core
   b. mantle
   c. skin
   d. crust

8. The core of the Earth is _____.

   a. rock
   b. liquid
   c. ice
   d. none of the above

Hint: Rocks are made up of minerals. Many things that people use are made from the minerals in rocks.

Mark the object that is a mineral product.

1. a. apple
   b. gold jewelry
   c. book
   d. fish

2. a. soda can
   b. newspaper
   c. peach
   d. envelope

3. a. china teapot
   b. cotton dress
   c. wooden house
   d. none of the above

4. a. penny
   b. dictionary
   c. cookie
   d. none of the above

5. a. metal scissors
   b. math book
   c. tomato
   d. none of the above

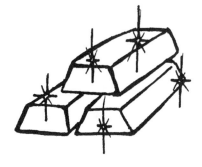

Hint: We use air, water, soil, rocks, and minerals from the Earth. We need to take care of the earth and save the natural resources.

Choose the best word to fill in the blank.

1. Turn off the _____ while you brush your teeth.

    a. water
    b. light
    c. noise
    d. music

2. Turn off the _____ you are not using.

    a. books
    b. lights
    c. food
    d. none of the above

3. _____ paper, cans, and glass.

    a. Toss
    b. Recycle
    c. Eat
    d. None of the above

4. _____ trees and grass and flowers.

    a. Cook
    b. Read
    c. Eat
    d. Plant

2nd Grade Edition   98

Hint: Students should know that Earth's surface changes over time. The Earth's surface changes by processes including erosion, earthquakes, volcanoes, landslides, and floods.

1. An earthquake is _____.

    a. a big storm
    b. the Earth moving
    c. thunder vibrating
    d. none of the above

2. The Richter Scale is used to _____.

    a. measure the strength of an earthquake.
    b. weigh the falling rocks
    c. measure the width of cracks
    d. none of the above

3. Most earthquakes occur in the Earth's _____.

    a. core
    b. crust
    c. mantle
    d. none of the above

4. Large sections of the Earth's crust are always moving. Sometimes, two sections push against each other. The place where they meet is called a(an) _____.

    a. ocean
    b. volcano
    c. fault
    d. cliff

5. Earthquakes can cause _____.

    a. dishes to break.
    b. buildings to fall down.
    c. cracks in streets.
    d. all of the above.

6. Dinosaurs were huge reptiles that lived on Earth for _____.

    a. millions of years.
    b. thousands of years.
    c. hundreds of years.
    d. none of the above.

7. When dinosaurs lived on earth, the world's oceans were _____.

    a. deeper and warmer
    b. shallower and warmer
    c. shallower and cooler
    d. none of the above

8. Dinosaur footprints, teeth, and bones are called _____.

    a. souvenirs
    b. fossils
    c. pieces
    d. none of the above

9. The huge meat-eating dinosaurs had _____.

    a. no brains
    b. large brains
    c. small brains
    d. two brains

10. Some plant-eating dinosaurs had an extra nerve center near their hips. It was used to _____.

    a. help them think
    b. help them move their tails and hind legs
    c. help them find food
    d. none of the above

11. Triceratops was a three-horned dinosaur that looked like a big _____.

    a. monkey
    b. shark
    c. rhinoceros
    d. none of the above

Hint: Students who use the scientific process ask meaningful questions and conduct investigations. Students should develop their own questions and perform experiments to test their hypotheses.

Second grade students should be able to measure length, weight, temperature, and liquid volume with appropriate tools and understand measurement in standard and non-standard units. Students should be able to construct bar graphs to understand data, using appropriate labels. Students should be able to write and draw a sequence of steps, events, and observations.

1. When ice cream melts, it changes from _____.
   a. a liquid to a gas.
   b. a liquid to a solid.
   c. a solid to a liquid.
   d. none of the above.

2. Anything that has weight and takes up space is _____.
   a. energy.
   b. matter.
   c. temperature.
   d. none of the above.

3. To measure how hot or cold it is outside, you use a _____.
   a. scale.
   b. ruler.
   c. thermometer.
   d. none of the above.

4. Which of the following gives us energy?
   a. watching a movie
   b. playing with the computer
   c. eating lunch
   d. none of the above

5. What causes ice to melt?
   a. sound
   b. heat
   c. electricity
   d. none of the above

6. Rocks, water, plants, and soil provide many resources for humans to use for_____.
   a. food and fuel
   b. computers and television
   c. cameras and radios
   d. none of the above

ANSWER KEY

SCIENCE

Physical Science
1. a
2. c
3. b
4. a
5. b
6. c
7. b

Life Science
1. c
2. b
3. a
4. a
5. a
6. c
7. a
8. b
9. c
10. b

Earth Science
1. b
2. a
3. b
4. c
5. b
6. a
7. b

8. b

1. b
2. a
3. a
4. a
5. a

1. a
2. b
3. b
4. d

1. b
2. a
3. b
4. c
5. d
6. a
7. b
8. b
9. c
10. b
11. c

1. c
2. b
3. c
4. c
5. b
6. a

SOCIAL SCIENCE

According to the California State Content Standards in History/Social Studies, students in the second grade learn about important people in the present day and the past. Students should differentiate between things that happened yesterday and long ago. They trace family history and compare the daily lives of their parents and grandparents.

Content Cluster: MAP READING

Objective: Students will demonstrate their understanding of map skills by locating on a grid system specific locations and geographic features of their neighborhood or community. They will understand essential map elements of title, scale, key, and directional indicator.

Parent Tip: Read about North America. Locate it on a world map and discuss it as the continent we live on.

North America is the third largest continent. On North America the three largest countries in order of size are Canada, the United States, and Mexico. There are also 20 other small countries, which include many Caribbean islands.

Climates in North America range from always cold in the far north to always hot and wet in the far south, with milder climates in between. There are many mountains, plains, deserts, and bodies of water in North America. The Pacific Ocean and Atlantic Ocean border the west and east sides of North America.

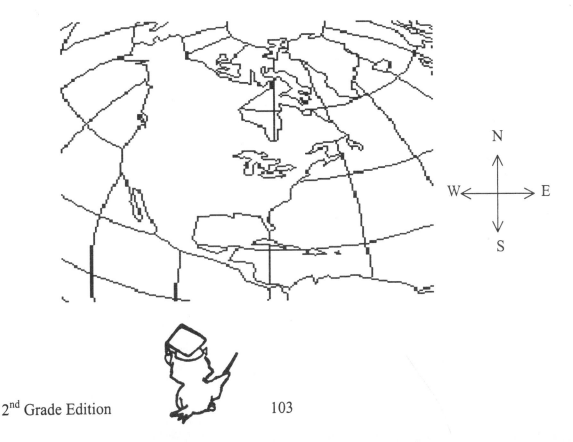

Choose the correct answer for the following questions.

1. North America is a _____.

    a. city
    b. country
    c. continent
    d. river

2. The United States, Canada, and _____ are the three largest countries in North America.

    a. France
    b. Mexico
    c. Africa
    d. Russia

3. The climate of North America can be hot, wet, cold, and _____.

    a. mountains
    b. rivers
    c. mild
    d. none of the above

4. There are mountains, plains, deserts, and _____ in North America.

    a. giraffes
    b. bodies of water
    c. koalas
    d. none of the above

5. The ocean on the west side of North America is the _____.

    a. Atlantic
    b. Indian
    c. Pacific
    d. Dead Sea

Many maps and globes have a grid line that divides the earth into two equal parts. It is called the <u>equator</u>. The equator helps people read maps. It is not a real line you can touch on the earth.

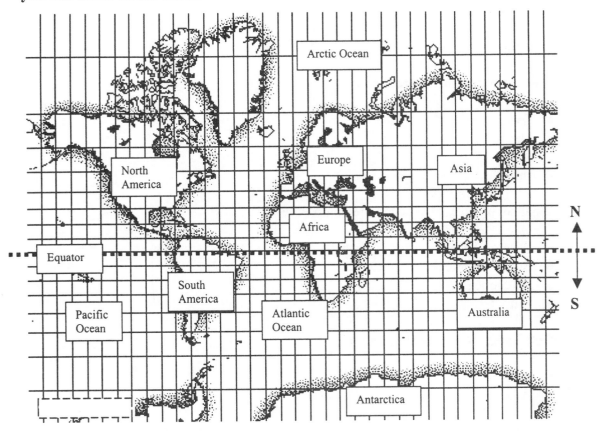

Use the above map to answer the following questions.

1. I am south of the equator and the smallest continent. I am _____.

   a. Europe
   b. Australia
   c. North America
   d. Asia

2. I am an imaginary line in the middle of the world. I am _____.

   a. the Pacific Ocean
   b. the Arctic Ocean
   c. the equator
   d. the North Pole

3. The largest ocean in the world is the _____.

   a. Pacific
   b. Atlantic
   c. Indian
   d. Arctic

4. How many continents are there?

   a. five
   b. six
   c. seven
   d. nine

5. What continent is also called the South Pole?

   a. Asia
   b. South America
   c. Antarctica
   d. Europe

6. I am China. What continent am I?

   a. Asia
   b. Africa
   c. North America
   d. South America

7. On which continent is the United States located?

   a. South America
   b. North America
   c. Asia
   d. Europe

HINT: Second grade students should know about contributions of men and women who lived long ago and in recent past history, e.g., scientists and inventors such as Newton, Galileo, George Washington Carver, Thomas Edison, and Albert Einstein.

Answer the following questions by choosing the correct answer.

1. George Washington Carver was a famous American scientist. He invented hundreds of ways to use _____.

    a. eggs
    b. peanuts
    c. horses
    d. cars

2. Benjamin Franklin was a great inventor. What was one of his famous inventions?

    a. bifocal eyeglasses
    b. rockets
    c. the car
    d. the telephone

3. Thomas Edison's most important inventions was the _____.

    a. television
    b. book
    c. electric light bulb
    d. automobile

4. The Wright Brothers flew the first airplane about _____ years ago.

    a. 100
    b. 200
    c. 50
    d. 150

5. Amelia Earhart is known for her accomplishments as a _____.

    a. nurse
    b. pilot
    c. doctor
    d. farmer

Content Cluster: GOVERNMENT

Objective: Students will understand the basic institutions and practices of government.

> **Parent Tip:** Select a variety of grade level appropriate fiction and nonfiction books about our government.

Read about the President's job and answer the questions.

The President is the head of the United States government. As leader of the government, the President has the most important job in the country. The American people vote for, or elect, the President. Every four years there is an election to decide who will be President. Once elected, the President holds office for a term of four years. A President cannot serve more than two terms.

1. The President is the _____ of the government.
   a. head
   b. money
   c. law
   d. none of the above

2. The President is _____ .
   a. nice
   b. elected
   c. tall
   d. none of the above

3. The President holds office for _____ years.
   a. three
   b. four
   c. two
   d. eight

4. The President can serve for _____ terms.
   a. two
   b. four
   c. six
   d. three

5. American people _____ to choose the President.
   a. sing
   b. talk
   c. vote
   d. none of the above

Read about our government. Then, answer the questions by choosing the best answer.

The government of the United States is a democracy. Democracy means "rule by the people." In the United States, Americans vote for, or elect, people to run the government. The people who are elected work to keep America strong. They also work to protect the rights of all Americans.

1. People who live in the United States are called

    a. men.
    b. Americans.
    c. women.
    d. none of the above

2. "protect" means

    a. keep safe
    b. be careful
    c. go slow
    d. none of the above

3. "elect" means

    a. think about
    b. play with
    c. vote for
    d. none of the above

4. The kind of government in the United States is a

    a. democracy.
    b. kingdom.
    c. athletic.
    d. none of the above

Second grade students should be able to describe how climate, weather, and availability of resources affect the crops a farmer can grow.

Answer the following questions by choosing the correct answer.

1. Peanut plants need _____ while blooming and forming buds.

   a. hot weather and moisture
   b. cold weather and wind
   c. hot weather and no water
   d. none of the above

2. The soil in which a peanut is planted needs to be _____.

   a. hard and dry
   b. warm and moist
   c. soft and dry
   d. none of the above

3. The soil should be _____ before planted.

   a. plowed
   b. used for horses
   c. cooled
   d. none of the above

4. Peanuts are harvested by _____.

   a. ox carts
   b. mechanical diggers
   c. horse plows
   d. none of the above

5. Peanuts can be made into _____.

   a. two or three products
   b. twenty products
   c. hundreds of products
   d. none of the above

ANSWER KEY

SOCIAL SCIENCE

Map Reading
1. c
2. b
3. c
4. b
5. c

1. b
2. c
3. a
4. c
5. c
6. a
7. b

Famous Americans
1. b
2. a
3. c
4. a
5. b

Government
1. a
2. b
3. b
4. a
5. c

1. b
2. a
3. c
4. a

1. a
2. b
3. a
4. b
5. c

ADDITIONAL TEACHING TIPS...

English/Language Arts Writing Standards

Students in Grade 2 need to develop writing strategies that include the stages of the writing process (e.g., prewriting, drafting, revising, and editing successive versions).

✓ Students should group related ideas and maintain a consistent focus.

✓ Students should create readable documents with legible penmanship.

✓ Students should understand the purposes of various reference materials (e.g., dictionary, thesaurus, and atlas).

✓ Students should revise original drafts to improve sequence and provide descriptive details.

Literary Response and Analysis of Grade-Level-Appropriate Test

Students should read and respond to a wide variety of children's literature. They need to understand structural features and elements such as theme, plot, setting, and characters.

✓ Students should compare and contrast plots, settings, and characters as presented by different authors.

✓ Students should compare and contrast different versions of the same stories that reflect different cultures.

✓ Students should identify use of rhythm, rhyme, and alteration in poetry.

✓ Students should retell stories in sequence and include facts, and details.

JUST FOR FUN!

Fill in the bubbles next to the correct answer.

1. What are the three states of water?

    a. ⬭ solid, gas, liquid

    b. ⬭ liquid, rain, wood

    c. ⬭ gas, soil, glass

2. What are the three types of rocks?

    a. ⬭ orange, pink, white

    b. ⬭ igneous, sedimentary, metamorphic

    c. ⬭ hard, solid, soil

3. What is it called when a green plant makes food from the sun?

    a. ⬭ condensation

    b. ⬭ evaporation

    c. ⬭ photosynthesis

4. What are the five senses?

    a. ⬭ sight, smell, touch, taste, hearing

    b. ⬭ penny, dime, quarter, nickel, dollar

    c. ⬭ orange, apple, lime, lemon, peach

5. What type of animal has scales and breathes air?

    a. ⬭ gorilla

    b. ⬭ reptile

    c. ⬭ fish

6. What type of animal produces milk for its babies?

    a. ⬭ bird

    b. ⬭ snake

    c. ⬭ mammal

7. What are five things living things need to survive?

    a. ⬭ space, air, water, food, shelter

    b. ⬭ soil, sand, water, plants, air

    c. ⬭ color, sun, moon, grass, air

8. Halloween falls in what season?

    a. ⬭ summer

    b. ⬭ spring

    c. ⬭ autumn

9. The temperature outside is usually highest in what season?

    a. ⬭ winter

    b. ⬭ fall

    c. ⬭ summer

10. What food is most healthy?

    a. ⬭ milk

    b. ⬭ candy

    c. ⬭ ice cream

ANSWERS   1. a   6. c
          2. b   7. a
          3. c   8. c
          4. a   9. c
          5. b   10. a

NOTES

NOTES

NOTES

NOTES

NOTES

NOTES